ETERNALOONS

The Palnik Anthology

To Diana in
friendship.....

Palnik
93

ETERNALOONS

The Palnik Anthology

By

Paul Palnik

Creative Light Press
Columbus, Ohio
5751-1991

To THE CREATOR in my beautiful wife Nancy, and in my precious children, Matthew, Judah, Elijah and Naomi.

FOREWARD

"There is no malice in the gentle art of Paul Palnik." I first wrote those words for Paul's master's thesis exhibition at Ohio State University in 1969. Fifteen years later, these words still have relevance to his quietly raucous visual overview of the human comedy.

Paul Palnik's cartoon style is readily understood by its symbolic form. Although he has demonstrated that he can draw and paint in other contemporary modes, his choice of the common cartoon image is deliberate. He is truly a child of the TV generation, and his visual and pictorial inspiration is the animated TV commercial cartoon.

It is interesting to note the career of yet another successful former student and colleague, Roy Lichtenstein. Roy's work is acknowledged as high art while Paul is content with success as a popular artist. Yet both began their early careers influenced by the immediately accessible popular advertisements — illustrated catalogues, cartoon strips, popular romances. For example, Roy Lichtenstein's *Masterpeice,* an oil painting of 1962, depicts "Barbie" and "Ken" types in a cartoon panel format. Barbie is "saying" in her balloon: "THIS PAINTING IS A *MASTERPIECE!* MY, SOON YOU'LL HAVE ALL OF *NEW YORK* CLAMORING FOR YOUR WORK."

Paul Palnik's *Someday I'm gonna own this town!! (Yes, indeedy do),* expresses the same confident notion that dreams can become reality. While the text has disappeared from Lichtenstein's work, its role in Paul Palnik's drawings continues unabated.

What the Currier and Ives prints were to the 19th century, Palnik prints seem to be to our time. But unlike the Currier and Ives documentations which depicted race horses, steamboats, fires and other catastrophies, the Palnik prints deal with people—the long, the tall, the short, the lean, the fat—the war between the sexes, humanity with all of its inspired yearnings and its feral reality.

Paul's generation was weaned on television and his lifelong exposure has ingrained indelibly on his awareness that life includes constipation, headaches, hemorrhoidal discomforts among a long list of "easily" remedied ailments. Paul's people allow us to examine these realities with a humorous light approach that makes us aware of life's rich possibilities within ourselves. He tells us that despite bad cooking, belching, zits, nose picking and the additional alimentary canal dramas, we are, or may be, beautiful. These and other human factors are communicated by "just some lines on paper," as Pitzel, the character in his *PITZEL* poster tells us. How we live our lives is how we live our lives.

The moral imperative underscores all of Palnik's outrageously absurd humor. *"SHAPETH UP...AND GETETH THINE ACT TOGETHER!!!"*, a bearded figure on the mount tells the assembled multitudes. Clearly faith — the Old Testament kind — is his message. *FREEDOM* recalls the parting of the Red Sea; *JUDGEMENT* wittily parodies the medieval didactic prints of Judgement Day, Redemption and Damnation. Verily, some of us will never make it to heaven.

Even Michelangelo's Sistine Chapel paintings of Creation are not immune to Palnik's pen. In the poster, *BE UNIQUE,* the pointing hand emerges amidst thunderbolts with the message: BE UNIQUE HAVE A MYSTICAL REVELATION FROM GOD, to a very benign recipient.

The posters multiply to my pleasure. Each new one provides surprises and humor which are sometimes painfully profound in their impact. *LIFE IS THE MUSIC AND NOBODY CAN RESIST DANCING* catalogs various ways humanity comes to terms with life, beginning with **"The dance of the dancers who dance in order to dance. They dance because they dance,"** and ends with **"Dance of the depressed, worried and self-pitying with befuddled lives and confused priorities...What a shame!"**

PROVERBS **(The wise are happy and fools know not why),** best sums up the artist's philosophy and purpose. "Faith can cause an artist like Paul Palnik ©1983–5743 to create a PROVERBS poster and actually believe (very strongly) that his poster will cause happiness and make this world a little better place to live in," he communicates.

All that sums up pretty much what kind of person Paul Palnik is. The lines between confidence and inanity, banality and profundity, are very thin ones indeed. For me, a Palnik poster transcends its genre and becomes a poem, or a religious tome translated into the vulgate. What kind of person would make a poster such as, *Hi world, I'm ME!?*

If I had to choose only one poster, my choice would be *PITZEL,* because in it Palnik's genius explicates the reality of graphic communication possibilities. The magic of perception is marvelously demonstrated with wit, humor and simplicity. The rich possibilities of human understanding are visualized in a manner which is open-ended by its imagination.

Here is an artist who understands the power of faith and love. When I first wrote about his gentle art, he already had decided on what kind of artist he wanted to be. As a teacher, my purpose always has been to encourage uniqueness, to provide the kind of environment in which creativity might occur. Paul Palnik was one of the few who were content to do their own thing. He had the confidence, imagination and intelligence to do it.

Indeed, these Palnik Posters are truly without malice. I believe they are a valid form of art. In a culture which classifies art as high and low, popular and arcane, I am reminded of a *New York Times* review of an exhibition of Saul Steinberg's drawings. The critic concluded his observations with: "Is it art?" "No." "Is it art?" "Yes."

So we must decide for ourselves. Examine these gentle drawings of Paul Palnik and enjoy.

Sidney Chafetz
Professor Emeritus of Art
Ohio State University
Columbus, Ohio

"I want to cause people to feel, to think and to wonder about our place in the universe and our ultimate role in eternity. By contrasting profound with absurd, knowledge with ignorance, purposefulness with aimlessness, I hope to clear the way for a better understanding of who we are and what we can become, both positive and negative. The future belongs to the one, most fully alive in the present."

PAUL PALNIK

ETERNALOONS

The Palnik Anthology

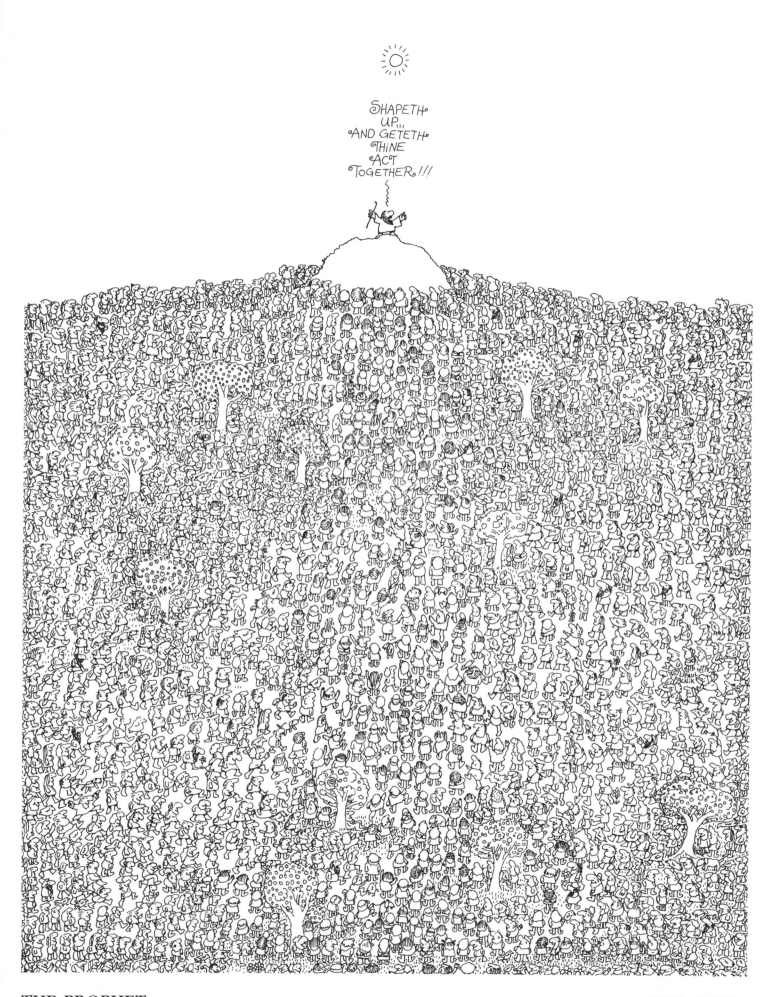

THE PROPHET   5738–1978

JUDGEMENT

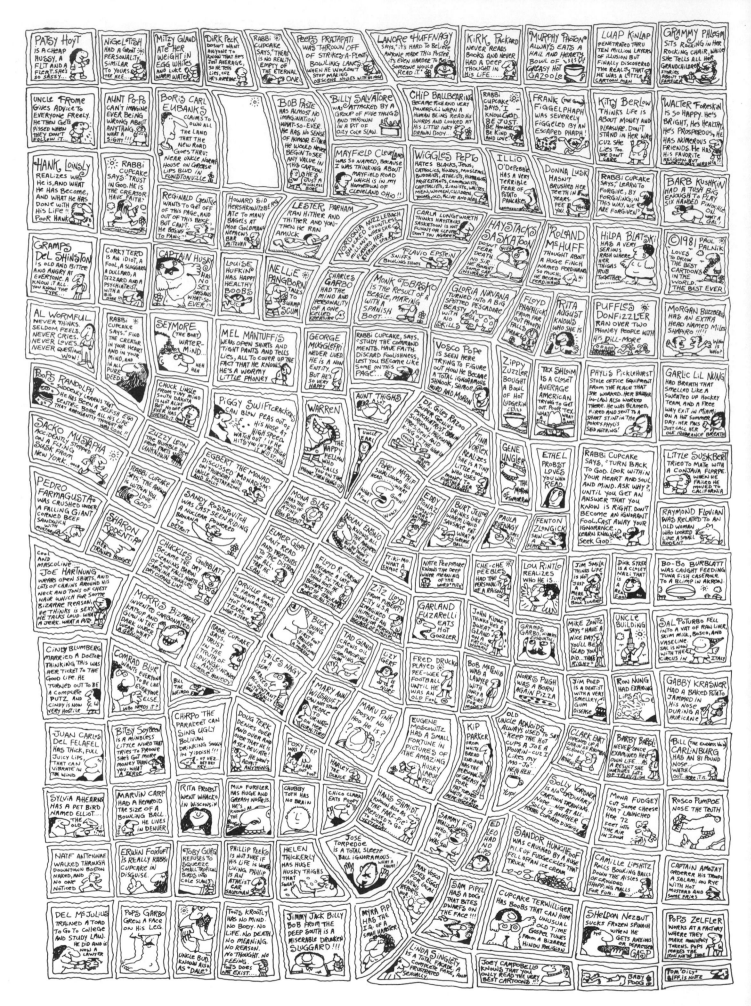

CHARACTERS

5741–1981

CREATION OF HUMANITY OUT OF NOTHINGNESS 5738–1978

DANCING – (LIFE IS THE MUSIC) 5743–1983

FREEDOM

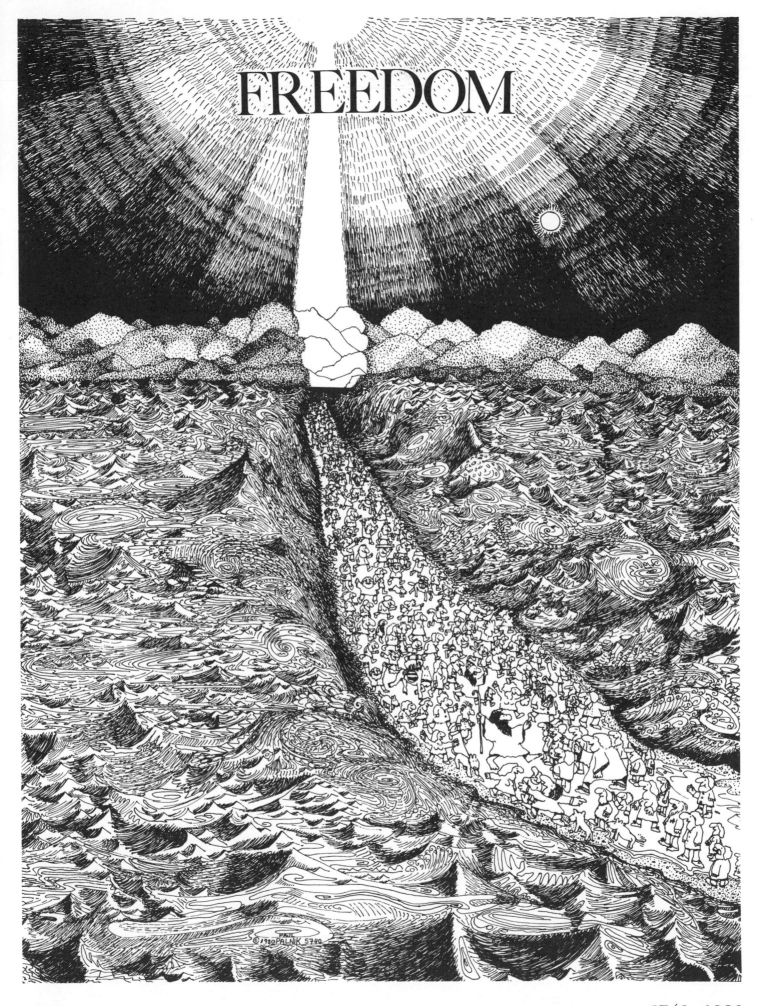

FREEDOM

5740–1980

WEATHER
HAIL STONES THE SIZE OF UNRIPE SMALL PUMPKINS WILL FALL TODAY, BUT THIS WILL GO AWAY AND THEN IT WILL BE REAL SUNNY. HIGH IN THE 80s, LOW 35. SEE MAP

THE pooplar POST

FINAL EDITION
BOOGER PRESS INTERNATIONAL.
CRAZEO NEWSPEOPLE ASSOC.
FURF-PIE TIMES NEWS SERVICE
YUCKA PUCKA POO PRESS

56 PAGES — THE MOST DELUXE NEWS THERE IS. — 4 SECTIONS

VOLUME 5740, NUMBER 1.   POOPLAR FALLS, OHIO 43219. MONDAY, SEPTEMBER 24, 2019   ©1980 PAUL PALNIK   15 CENTS

USA CAPITAL MOVES TO POOPLAR FALLS.

BY PIGGY SWIFTCRACKERS

WASHINGTON — WHILE THE CABINET VOTED ON THE AMAZING DECISION TO MOVE OUR NATIONS CAPITAL TO POOPLAR FALLS OHIO, THOUSANDS RAN AMUCK OUTSIDE THE WHITE HOUSE IN A DESPERATE ATTEMPT TO PROTEST THE MOVE. SOME CLAIMED THAT PRESIDENT FECAL WAS ACTING INSANELY, AND THAT HE HAD NO AUTHORITY TO MAKE THE MOVE. ONE MAN WHO WAS DRAGGED SCREAMING AND KICKING FROM THE WHITE HOUSE PARKING LOT, CHANTED "FLUSH FECAL" OVER AND OVER. POLICE ARRESTED ELEVEN TEACHERS FROM DETROIT WHEN THEY DROVE THEIR RENTED TRUCK INTO VICE PRESIDENT POKERBURG'S CAR. THE VICE PRESIDENT AND MRS. POKERBURG WERE NOT INJURED.

HOARDS OF PROTESTING CITIZENS RUN AMUCK AND HIGGELTY-PIGGELTY OUTSIDE THE WHITE HOUSE......

AROUND TOWN

CARMINE LUFFMILK FOUND A CUP OF STEAMIN' HOT JO ON HER BACK PORCH. HAIL'N HEARTY!

CASPER RANCHLIPS, OF ELEVENTH AVE CLAIMS TO HAVE BOWLED TWO PERFECT 300 GAMES AT "STRIKES-A-PLENTY LANES" IN RAYMONVILLE. NO ONE WAS ABLE TO BACK UP CASPER'S CLAIM AND SEVERAL OTHER BOWLERS CALLED CASPER A CHEAP LIAR AND A DISGUSTING FRAUD.

MICKEY POOGHAMMER, WAS KNOCKED OFF HIS BIKE BY AN UNIDENTIFIED PERSON WHO THOUGHT HE WAS A POOPLAR POST DELIVERY BOY.

FREDONIA ARGH, WAS VOTED WOMAN OF THE YEAR BY THE "BIG THIGHS LEAGUE" OF WEST POOPLAR FALLS.

RAYMOND POUND, GOT PUNCHED OFF HIS FEET BY A LOITERER IN FRONT OF THE ROTO-ROOTER STORE.

CHITO LOBES FOUND AN ANTIQUE CHAIR DESIGNED BY SWEEDISH ARTISAN SOØVEN KIERKER SVENSON. THE CHAIR IS OVER 600 YEARS OLD, AND IS VALUED AT OVER ONE MILLION DOLLARS.

FATTY RATOOG WAS THROWN VIOLENTLY AGAINST A WALL FOUR TIMES BY ENRAGED ANTIQUE OWNER, CHITO LOBES. FATTY SMASHED MR. LOBES PRIZED SWEEDISH CHAIR WHEN HE SAT ON IT WHILE MAKING A PHONE CALL. FATTY IS RECOVERING AT SAINT THYROID OF THE HOLY GLAND HOSPITAL.

PUMPKIN TISH OF ELVIRA STREET FOUND HER LOST DOG SWIFTY. SWIFTY WAS MISSING FOR THREE MONTHS. PUMPKIN PRESUMED THAT SWIFTY WAS EITHER LOST OR STOLEN OR DEAD. SWIFTY CLAIMS THAT PUMPKIN IS SUCH A AGRAVATING PERSON THAT HE HAD TO FLEE TO A DISTANT LAND, SIMPLY FOR SOME PEACE OF MIND. PUMPKIN CLAIMS THAT SWIFTY DEFINATELY CAN NOT TALK...THE TWO WERE LAST SEEN RUNNING THROUGH FARMER BLUNG'S CORN FIELD.

AROUND THE WORLD

SHEIK PARDOZLE OF SAUDI ARABIA WAS MUGGED ON A RECENT VISIT TO CLEVELAND OHIO. WHEN ASKED ABOUT THE INCIDENT THE SHEIK SAID, "THEY GOT MY NEW WATCH?"

EDGAR E. PAPALOMA OF PARIS SAYS, "I THINK PRESIDENT FECAL IS A SELF SEEKING ROGUE, HE IS A SELF DESTRUCTIVE DIRTY RATTY CHEATY HATEY, STINKY; I DONT LIKE HIM AT ALL?"

THOUGHT FOR THE DAY

YOUR WHOLE LIFE HAS LED YOU TO THIS MOMENT, TO THESE EXACT WORDS. BEGIN THE REST OF YOUR LIFE WITH A HAPPY BLESSING.

THOSE DISAGREEING WITH THE PRESIDENT CLAIMED THAT POOPLAR FALLS WAS TO SMALL TO MOVE THE ENTIRE CAPITAL TO. SENATOR FULLFACE, DEMOCRAT FROM CALIFORNIA SAID, "I THINK WE SHOULD LEAVE THE CAPITAL EXACTLY WHERE IT IS." SENATOR THYMUS FROM DELEWARE CLAIMED THAT MUMFVILLE DELEWARE WAS BETTER THAN POOPLAR FALLS. "AFTER ALL", HE CONTINUED, "THERE'S NOTHING BUT A BUNCH OF MORONS IN POOPLAR FALLS. IT'S A TOWN INHABITED BY HICKS, IDIOTS, SLUGGARDS, DULLARDS, AND A WIDE ASSORTMENT OF BAFOONS. I SPEAK FOR ALL REPUBLICANS WHEN I SAY—THIS BIZARRE MOVE TO POOPLAR FALLS OHIO, IS A CLEAR INDICATION THAT THE PRESIDENT IS UNFIT TO LEAD OUR COUNTRY, AND IN FACT SHOULD BE SWIFTLY REMOVED FROM ALL POSITIONS OF AUTHORITY." ONE ENRAGED WOMAN FROM A LARGE INDUSTRIAL MIDWEST TOWN SAID "US RICH PEOPLE WANT A SOLID AND SECURE SYSTEM OF GOVERNMENT—PRESIDENT FECAL IS SUCH A FLAKE HEAD THAT THE AMERICAN PEOPLE DON'T KNOW WHAT HE'S GONNA DO NEXT. WE THOUGHT IT WAS STRANGE WHEN HE CALLED THE SOVIET FORIGN MINISTER A PUTZ, BUT WE SAID NOTHING, AND AFTER TWO YEARS OF THIS SORT OF THING — HE DECIDES TO MOVE THE CAPITAL TO SOME DINK TOWN." SPEAKER OF THE HOUSE SHEILAH PHOOPH, DEMOCRAT FROM PENNSYLVANIA ASKED THAT A MOTION BE MADE TO IMPEACH PRESIDENT FECAL.

POOPLAR HIGH FIGHTIN' TUSHS WIN SEASON OPENER

BY CHAD "LOINS" ZUZZBERGER
POOPLAR POST STAFF

SLUGGARD CORNERS - AFTER A DISASTEROUS SEASON LAST YEAR, AND STILL RECOVERING FROM THE INFAMOUS VASELINE INCIDENT, THE FIGHTIN' TUSHS "BEAT" THE BIG BROWN AND GREEN' FROM SLUGGARD CORNERS. THE SCORE WAS POOPLAR FALLS 38, SLUGGARD CORNERS 9. SOLLIE O'HENRY SCORED THREE TIMES FOR THE TUSHS, ON RUNS OF 7-18-AND 51 YDS. COACH NESTLEBROOK WAS EJECTED FROM THE GAME WHEN HE REFUSED TO PUT HIS PANTS BACK ON. HE REMOVED HIS PANTS IN PROTEST TO A 15 YD. PENALTY THAT WAS ASSESSED AGAINST KIRBY TINTORETTO FOR UNSPORTSMAN LIKE CONDUCT. KIRBY BROUGHT A SMALL METAL OBJECT ON TO THE FIELD AND HIT STUART RIZZIBERG ON THE HEAD WITH IT. RIZZIBERG, THE SLUGGARD CORNERS PLACE KICKER, CONNECTED ON 3 FIELD GOALS. TWO FANS FELL OUT OF THE UPPER DECK DURING THE BRU-HA-HA.

FOUR LANE NOW OPEN

BY NIPSY LAYDONKO - POOPLAR POST STAFF

DOZENS CHEERED IN GLEE...AS FORREST ADNOIDS, THE DEPUTY MAYOR OF POOPLAR FALLS OFFICIALLY OPENED THE NEW FOUR LANE HI-WAY THAT CONNECTS POOPLAR FALLS WITH COCKY HILLS. THE HI-WAY IS FOURTY FIVE MILES LONG AND WAS CONSTRUCTED AT A COST OF SOME OUTRAGEOUS SUM. AT 12:30 P.M. YESTERDAY FORREST ADNOIDS CUT THE RIBBON THAT SIGNALED TRAFFIC TO BEGIN USING THE FOUR LANE. ON HAND FOR THE EVENT WAS MONA NARPOPPO FROM THE CHAMBER OF COMMERCE—MS. NARPOPPO SAID,

"THIS NEW FOUR LANE WILL BE GOOD FOR ALL RESIDENTS OF OUR CITY BECAUSE IT IS A HI-WAY OF THE MIND AS WELL AS THE BODY—THE MIND AND BODY ARE ONE, AND NOW IS ETERNAL. THIS HI-WAY LEADS BEYOND TIME AND SPACE. MAY ALL WHO TRAVEL THIS HI-WAY KNOW PEACE, JOY, LOVE, KINDNESS AND GOODWILL. MAY GOD BLESS THE READER OF THESE WORDS. MAY YOU BECOME HEALTHY, WEALTHY, AND WISE. MAY MY WORK BRIGHTEN YOUR WAY?" DOZENS CHEERED IN GLEE, THEN THEY WENT HOME.

MAYOR GARBONZO
"WE WARMLY WELCOME PRESIDENT FECAL AND APPLAUD GTHIS COURAGEOUS DECISION".........

TWO MEN GIVEN THE McNULL AWARD

BY GLORIA "FIG" NEWTIN
POOPLAR POST STAFF

KENNY CHUMPMAN A BOOT LACKEY FROM THE SOUTHERN PART OF THE STATE AND LAZLO ZONTZ A BLIMP PILOT FROM AKRON, WERE AWARDED THE FAMED McNULL TROPHY FOR BRAVERY, WHEN THEY PULLED A LARGE MOLLUSK NAMESD BY GREGORY, OFF OF A SMALL CHILD IN ROPPO PARK YESTERDAY. IT SEEMS THE MOLLUSK ATTACKED THE TYKE BY THE SOUTH ENTRANCE TO THE PARK ON EIGHTH AVENUE. MR. CHUMPMAN HEARD THE CHILD SCREAMING AND RAN TO THE SCENE. MR. CHUMPMAN FOUGHT THE MOLLUSK OFF AND FREED THE WHIMPERING CHILD. THE TYKE LOST CONSCIOUSNESS AND SEEMED TO BE IN REAL DANGER... MEANWHILE LAZLO ZONTZ THE AKRON BRED BLIMP PILOT, SAW THE INCIDENT FROM HIS LOW FLYING BLIMP, LAZLO SWOOPED IN LOW AND PICKED UP KENNY CHUMPMAN AND THE CHILD AND RUSHED THEM TO FLANGE HOSPITAL. THE TYKE WAS REPORTED IN GOOD CONDITION BY A HOSPITAL SPOKESMAN THIS MORNING. MR. ZONTZ A NOTED EGOMANIAC MOUNTED HIS TROPHY ON TOP OF HIS BLIMP AND FLEW OFF SMILING. MR. CHUMPMAN WAS WHISKED OFF BY POLICE MOMENTS AFTER ACCEPTING THE REWARD—A POLICE SPOKESMAN SAID THAT MR. CHUMPMAN WAS WANTED IN 37 STATES FOR CRIMES RANGING FROM TRANSPORTING LARGE QUANTITIES OF SALMON PATTIES OVER INTERNATIONAL BOUNDARIES, TO MAKING A P-P IN THE STREET. AUTHORITIES CLAIMED THAT THE STREETS ARE SAFE FOR PEDESTRIANS AND CITIZENS SHOULD HAVE NO FEAR OF MOLLUSKA ATTACK.

POOPLAR FALLS MAYOR SPEAKS TO THE NATION

BY CHIP SCHWASTMILLER

POOPLAR FALLS- AS THIS BUCKEYE TOWN SLEPT PEACEFULLY NESTLED IN THE ROLLING FARM HILLS, ONE MAN; MAYOR EARL GARBONZO, WAS BUZILY PREPARING HIS STATEMENT THAT HE WILL DELIVER TO THE NATION TONIGHT. SPEAKING ON A COAST TO COAST TELEVISION HOOK UP, THE MAYOR WILL ADDRESS THE AMERICAN PEOPLE ON THE CONTROVERSIAL MOVE OF THE NATION'S CAPITAL.

MAYOR GARBONZO TOLD THE POST, "WE WARMLY WELCOME PRESIDENT FECAL AND APPLAUD GTHIS COURAGEOUS DECISION." WHEN ASKED ABOUT CHARGES THAT PRESIDENT FECAL WAS BONKERS THE MAYOR SAID, "LET ME RESPOND AS A HUMAN BEING ON THAT QUESTION, AND NOT AS THE MAYOR OF THIS FINE CITY — PRESIDENT FECAL IS A VISIONARY. HE CAN SEE THE FUTURE AND HE KNOWS FOR REASONS LESSER MINDS CAN NOT COMPREHEND, THAT WASHINGTON MUST MOVE TO POOPLAR FALLS IN ORDER TO STOP A RAMBLING AND FRIGHTENING EVER GROWING, POWER HUNGRY, PEOPLE FORGETING, BUREAUCRACY."

OTHER SUPPORTERS OF THE MOVE TOLD THE POST THAT PRESIDENT FECAL WAS A GIANT UPON THE EARTH AND THAT HE WOULD GO DOWN IN HISTORY AS THE GREATEST POLITICAL LEADER IN THE HISTORY OF THE WORLD. THEY DISMISSED AS "A BUNCH OF B.S.", THE CHARGE THAT THE PRESIDENT WAS A SHNOOK!

THE MAYOR SAID HE WILL EMPHASIZE SEVERAL MAJOR POINTS IN HIS SPEECH THIS EVENING (1) THE SANITY AND CLEAR MINDEDNESS OF THE PRESIDENT. (2) THE LOFTY ETHICAL STANCE THE PRESIDENT OPERATES ON. (3) THE LONG RANGE WISDOM OF MOVING THE CAPITAL OUT OF WASHINGTON. (4) THE SUBLIME WISDOM AND FORESIGHT TO SELECT POOPLAR FALLS, OHIO. AS THE NEW NATIONS CAPITAL.

ACTRESS GAGS IN AWE.
SAYS OF CURRENT CONTROVERSIE,"LONG LIVE PRES. FECAL."

INSIDE THE POST

NEWS DIGEST AND COMPLETE INDEX ON PAGE A3

CARRIER DELIVERY

TO RECEIVE THE POST DELIVERED TO YOUR DOOR DAILY SIMPLY GRAB ONE OF THE DELIVERY BOYS OFF HIS BIKE AND SAY, HEY HEY HEY, GIMME YOUR DEE LIVERY OF THE POST TODAY. OR CALL OUR OFFICES AND ASK FOR BEANIE AND WE WILL PUT YOU ON OUR MAILING LIST AND DELIVER YOU THE POOPLAR POST. YOU'LL JUST LOVE THE POST. IT'S FILLED WITH ONLY THE MOST DELUXE NEWS. EXPAND YOUR MIND, DEEPEN YOUR SOUL, DISCOVER NEW HORIZONS OF LIFE REALIZATION, HAVE A GOOD LAUGH NOW AND THEN. NEVER GIVE UP HOPE, THE POOPLAR FALLS POST WILL CHEER YOUR WAY......

RITA ROBUSTO

BY MILT PECKADILLO

HOLLYWOOD CA.— ACTRESS RITA ROBUSTO, KNOWN AFFECTIONATELY AS THIGHS-A-PLENTY, IN TINSEL TOWN; GAGGED IN AWE AND DISBELIEF WHEN SHE WAS INFORMED THAT HER HOME TOWN, POOPLAR FALLS WAS TO BECOME THE NEW SEAT OF POWER AND GOVERNMENT. THE PLUMP AND PRECIOUS MISS WAS EATING A PIECE OF FATTY MEAT WHEN THE NEWS REACHED HER. "SHE GAGGED, HER EYES BULGED, SHE GURGLED AND FELL ACROSS HER KITCHEN TABLE," SAID OTTO WAHDIDDY, A LONG TIME FRIEND AND ADVISOR. AFTER GAGGING FOR ABOUT 3 MINUTES THE PIECE OF FATTY MEAT FLEW OUT OF HER MOUTH. WIPING THE GREASE FROM HER LIPS WITH A DISH TOWEL, RITA SAID, "LONG LIVE PRESIDENT FECAL."

RITA BEGAN MAKING PLANS TO LAUNCH A CAMPAIGN TO MOVE THE MOVIE INDUSTRY FROM HOLLYWOOD TO POOPLAR FALLS. MOTION PICTURE MOGUL MAX BIFRO QUICKLY HOPPED ON THE BANDWAGON AND URGED OTHER INDUSTRY EXECUTIVES TO JOIN THE CAMPAIGN.

ON THE LIGHTER SIDE

WHEN ARLO GUNHUFF OF THIRD STREET WAS ELEVEN YEARS OLD HE VOWED TO BECOME A COW BOY IN TEXAS. AMAZING AS IT SEEMS, TWENTY YEARS LATER ARLO BECAME CHAIRMAN OF A LARGE CORPORATION THAT HAS NOTHING TO DO WITH COWBOYS—SO ARLO DRESSES UP LIKE A COWBOY-HA HA.

THE ANIMALS NOAH LEFT BEHIND

5738–1978

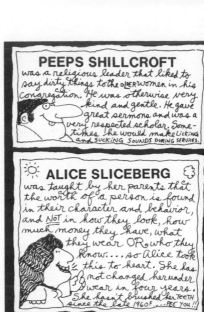

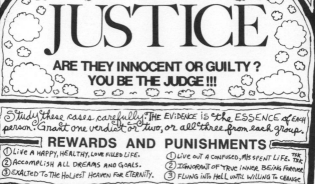

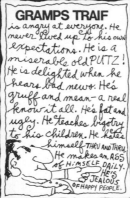

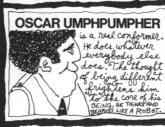

JUSTICE

5743–1983

STORYBOOK

BLESSINGS AND CURSES

OPTIMISTS
and
PESSIMISTS

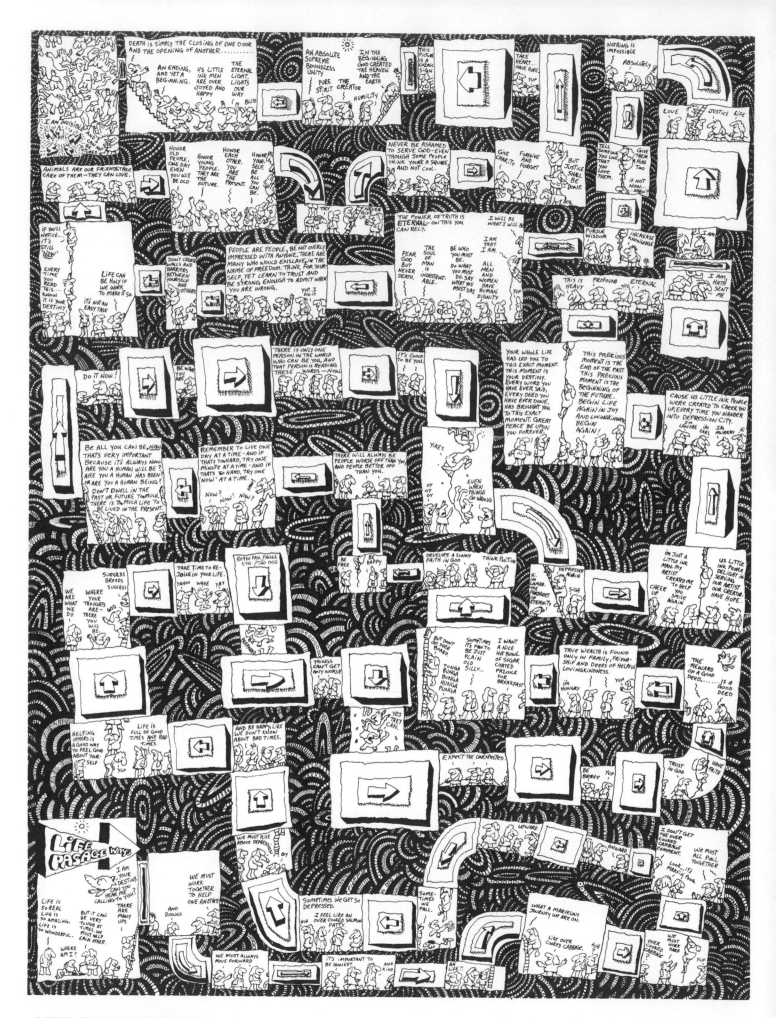

LIFE PASSAGEWAYS

5741–1980

SOMEDAY I'M GONNA OWN THIS TOWN 5738–1978

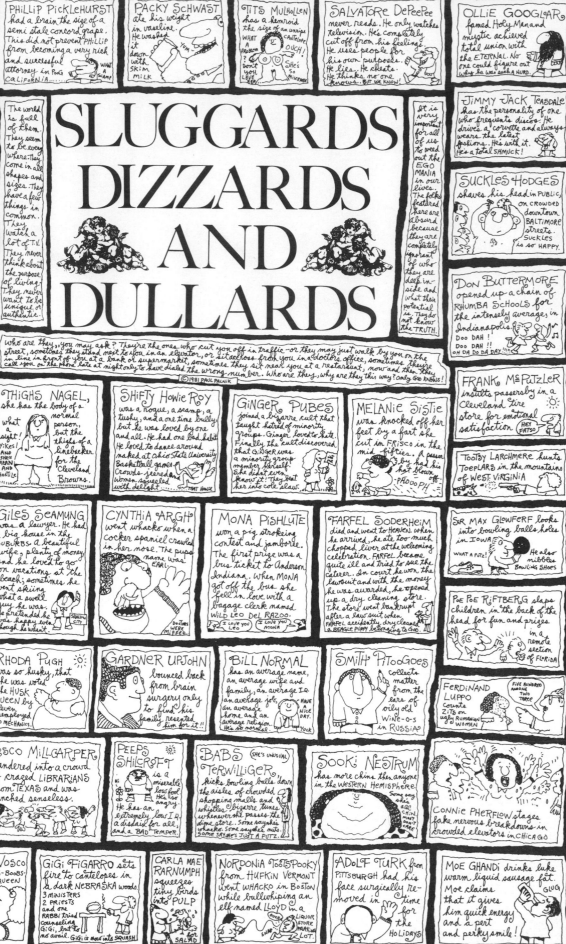

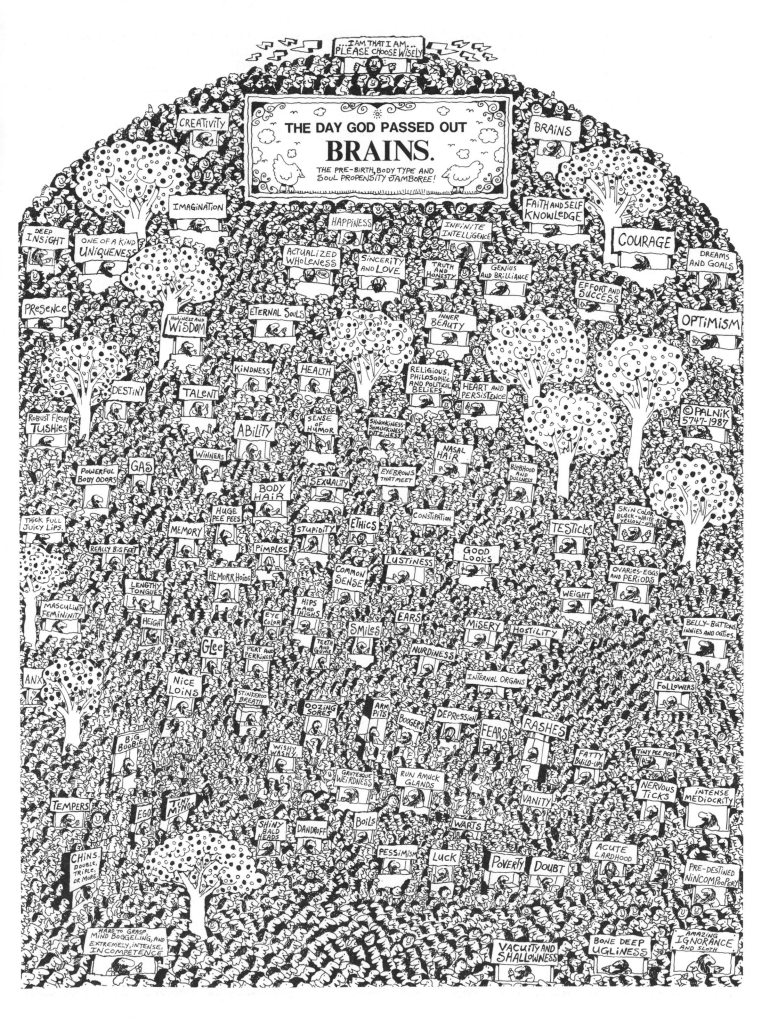

THE DAY GOD PASSED OUT BRAINS

5747-1987

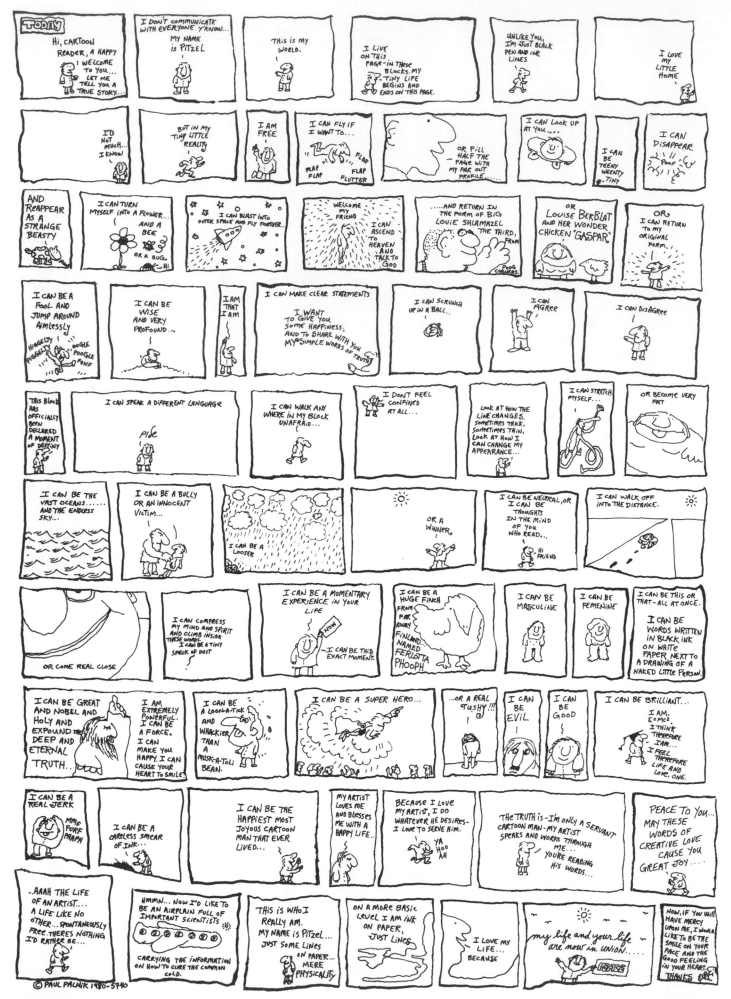

PITZEL

5740–1980

HI WORLD, I'M ME!

5738–1977

TO READ, OR NOT TO READ: (THAT IS THE QUESTION)   5740–1980

WE LOVE YOU

5740–1980

HAND WRITING

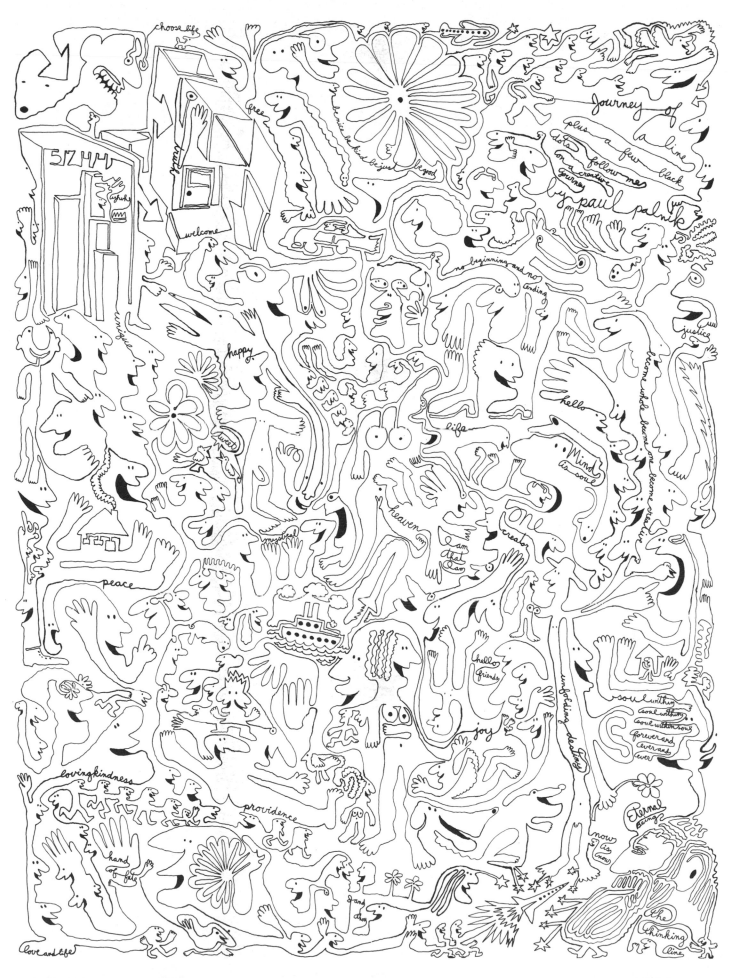

JOURNEY OF A LINE

5744–1983

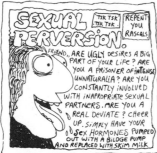

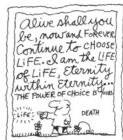

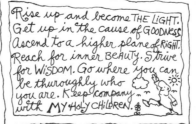

THE TINY INKMAN'S CREATOR 5747–1987

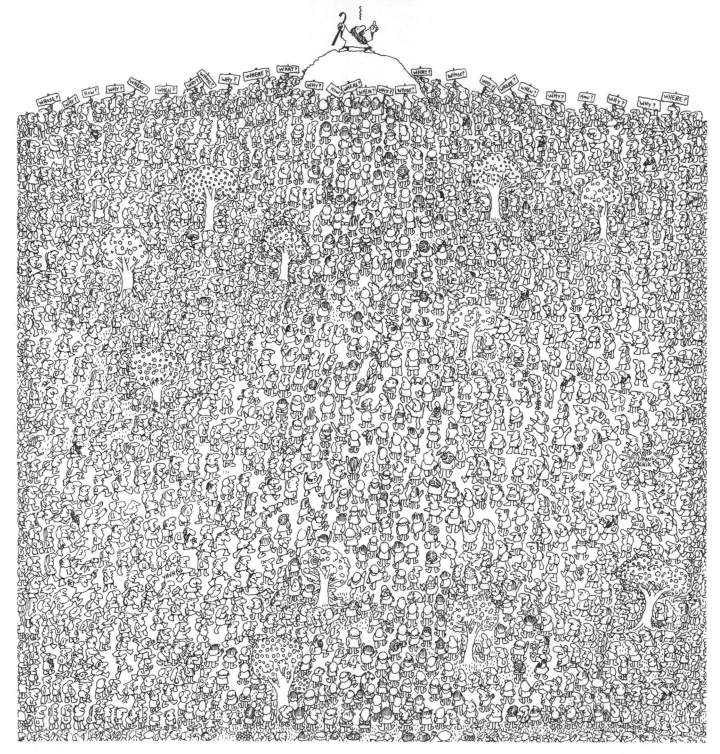

QUESTION AUTHORITY

LEVELS

5742–1981

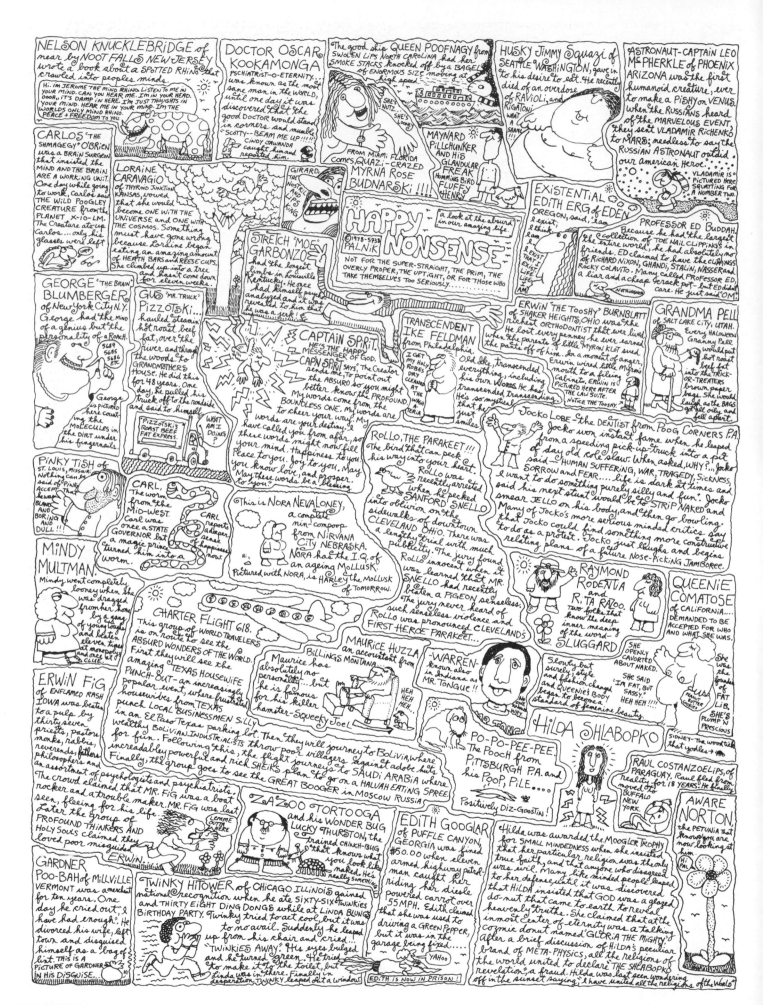

HAPPY NONSENSE

COUPLES (HOW TWO WORLDS BECOME ONE)   5740–1980

THE STADIUM OF LIFE

5739–1979

PROVERBS

5743–1983

OUR HOUSE

GOD BLESS OUR COZY HOME

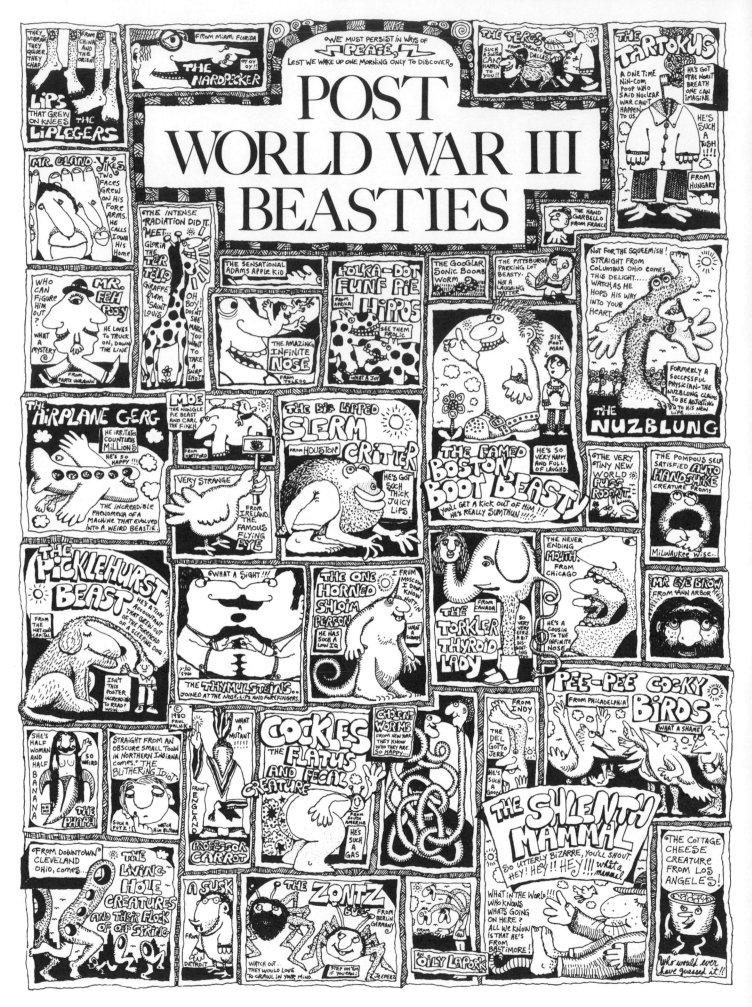

POST WORLD WAR III BEASTIES

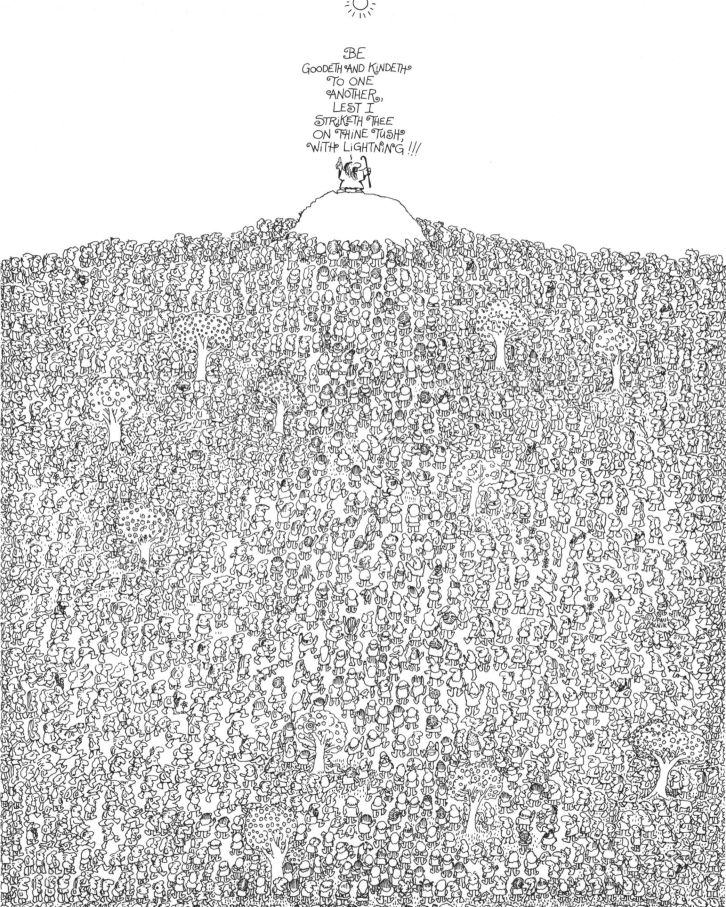

THINE TUSH

5742—1982

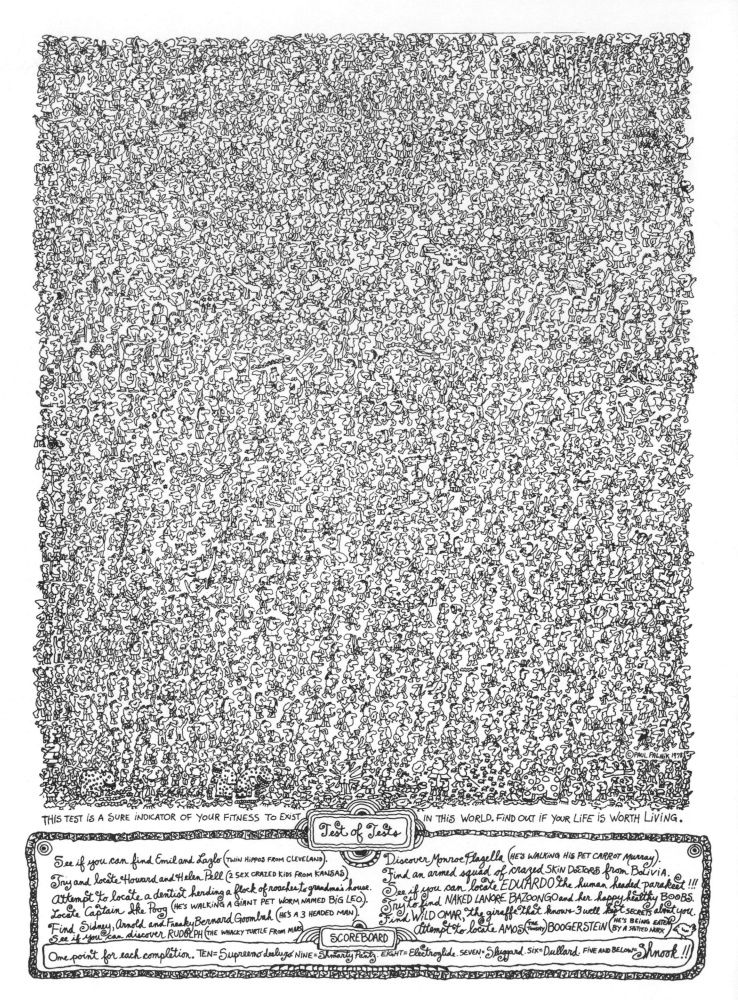

THIS TEST IS A SURE INDICATOR OF YOUR FITNESS TO EXIST *Test of Tests* IN THIS WORLD. FIND OUT IF YOUR LIFE IS WORTH LIVING.

See if you can find Emil and Lazlo (TWIN HIPPOS FROM CLEVELAND).
Try and locate Howard and Helen Pell (2 SEX CRAZED KIDS FROM KANSAS).
Attempt to locate a dentist herding a flock of roaches to grandma's house.
Locate Captain Ike Poog (HE'S WALKING A GIANT PET WORM NAMED BIG LEO).
Find Sidney, Arnold and Freaky Bernard Goombah (HE'S A 3 HEADED MAN).
See if you can discover RUDOLPH (THE WHACKY TURTLE FROM MARS).

Discover Monroe Flagella (HE'S WALKING HIS PET CARROT Murray).
Find an armed squad of crazed SKIN DOCTORS from BOLIVIA.
See if you can locate EDUARDO the human headed parakeet !!!
Try to find NAKED LANORE BAZOONGO and her happy healthy BOOBS.
Find WILD OMAR, the giraffe that knows 3 well kept secrets about you.
Attempt to locate AMOS (THE TOUCHY) BOOGERSTEIN (HE'S BEING EATEN BY A SPOTTED NURK).

SCOREBOARD

One point for each completion. TEN= Supreemo deeluxo. NINE= Shmarty Pants. EIGHT= Electroglide. SEVEN= Sluggard. SIX= Dullard. FIVE AND BELOW= Shnook !!!

TEST OF TESTS 5738–1978

THE VICTORY

THE VICTORY   5740–1980

MISGUIDED RELIGIOUS LEADERS   5739–1979

SAINTS MARCHING IN

5743–1983

LITTLE NAKEDS

5750–1990

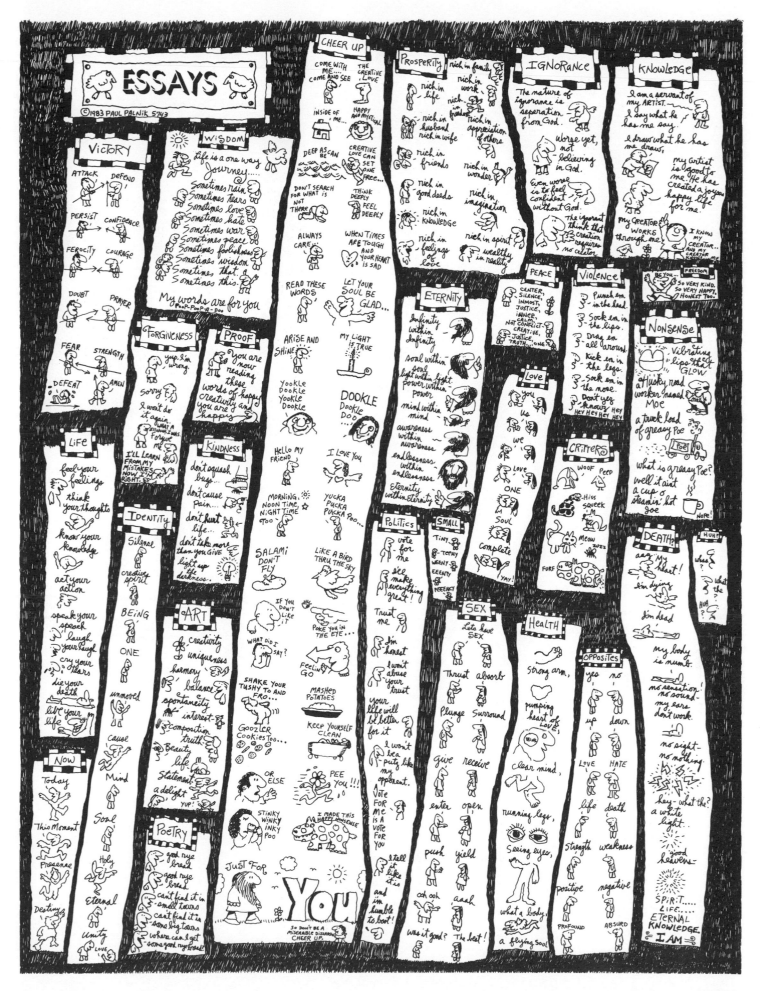

ESSAYS

5743–1983

PERSISTENCE

5750–1990

YES

5750–1990

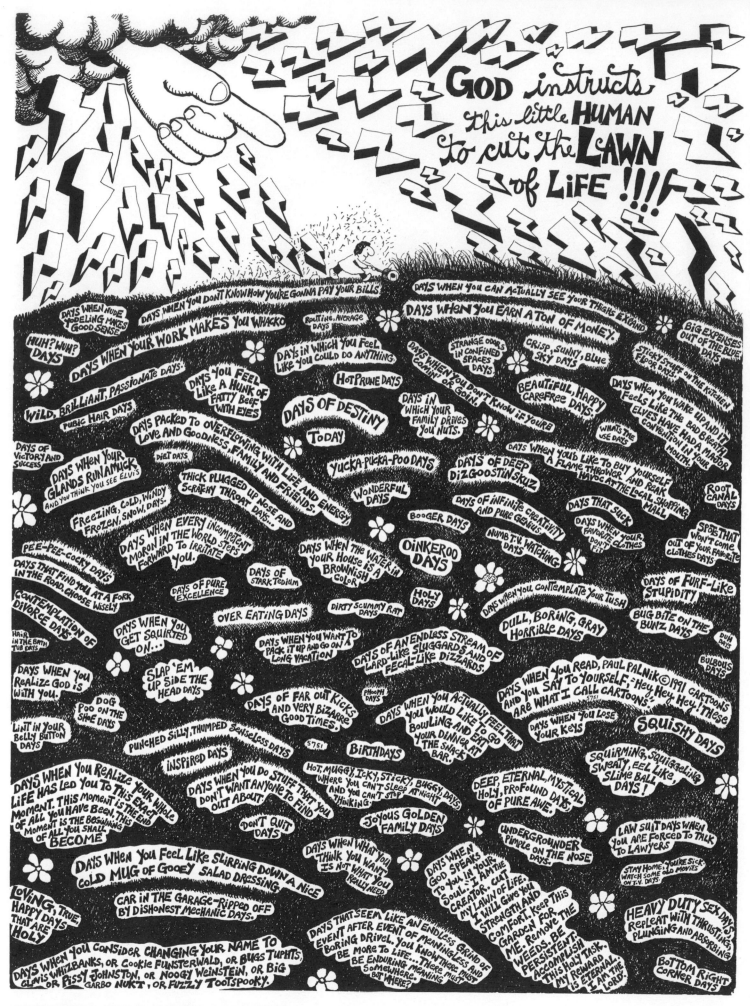

CUTTING THE LAWN OF LIFE

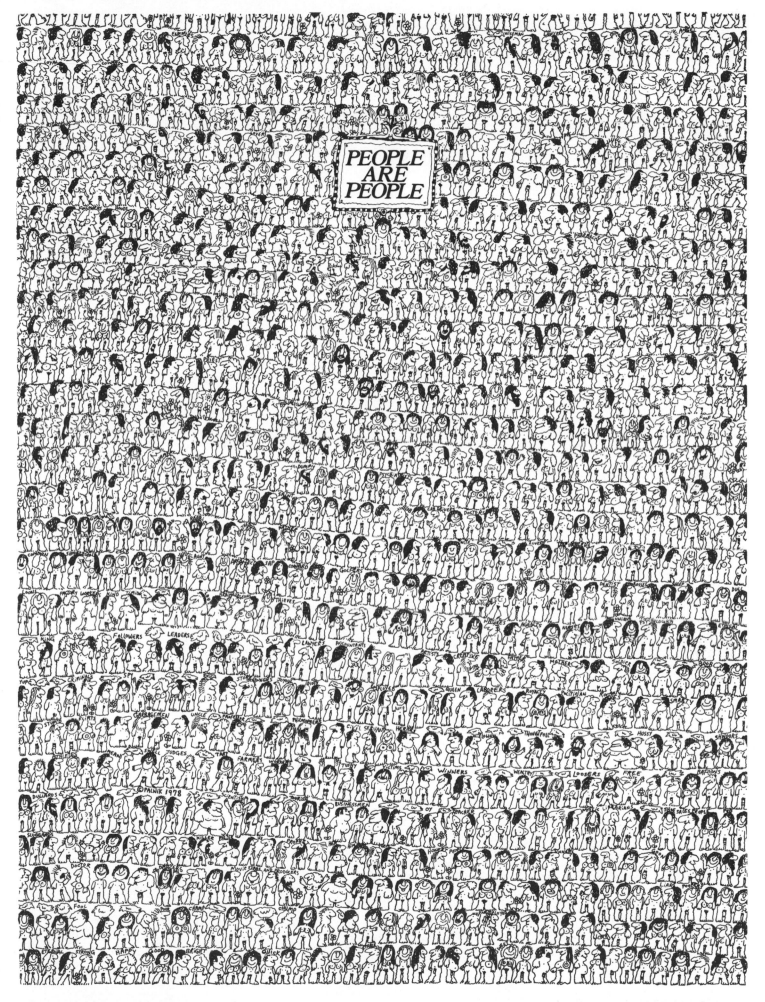

PEOPLE ARE PEOPLE

LIBERATED WOMEN'S ACROBATIC TEAM

5739–1979

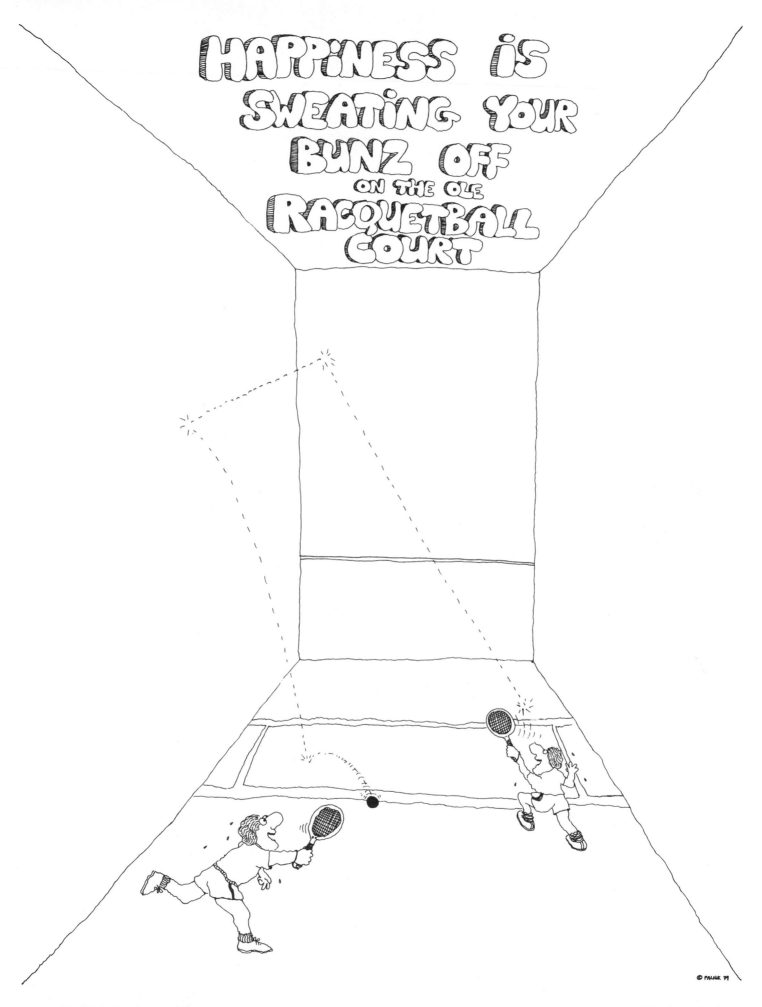

RACQUETBALL BUNZ

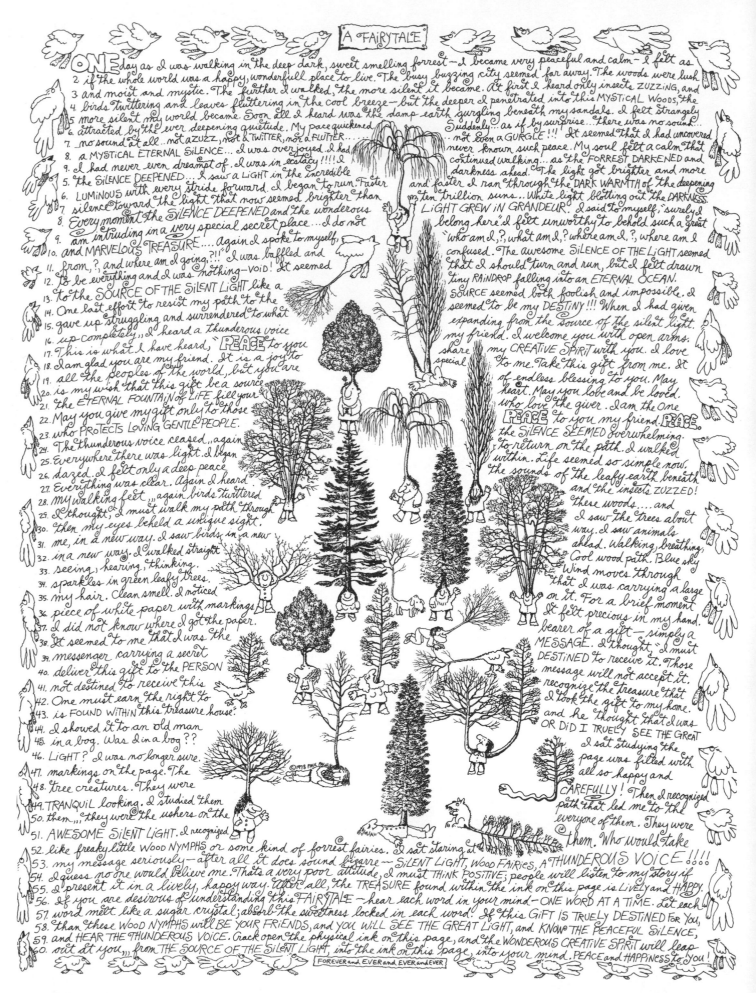

A FAIRYTALE

I LOVE TO SKI

5739–1979

ANGELS

5740–1980

GOD IN THE U.S.A. (ANTHROPOMORPHIC HI-JINX)

5750–1989

Autobiography

CREATIVE WILL

5751–1990

MEMORIAL

5744–1983

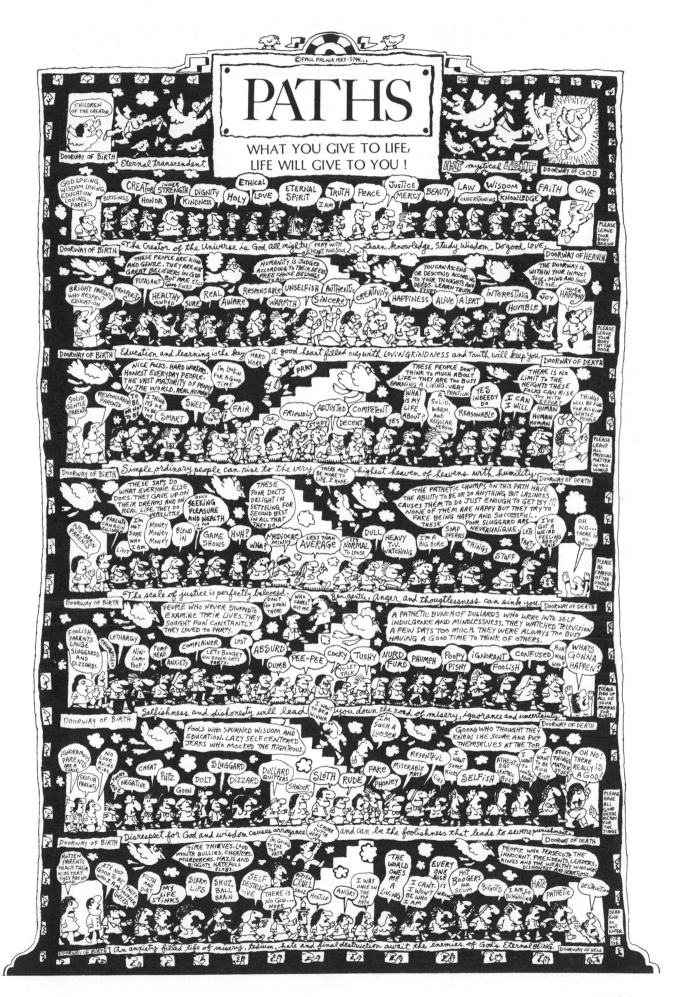

BIRTHDAY PRESENT

The Path of Success

THE PATH OF SUCCESS

5740–1980

THE SEARCH FOR IDEAS

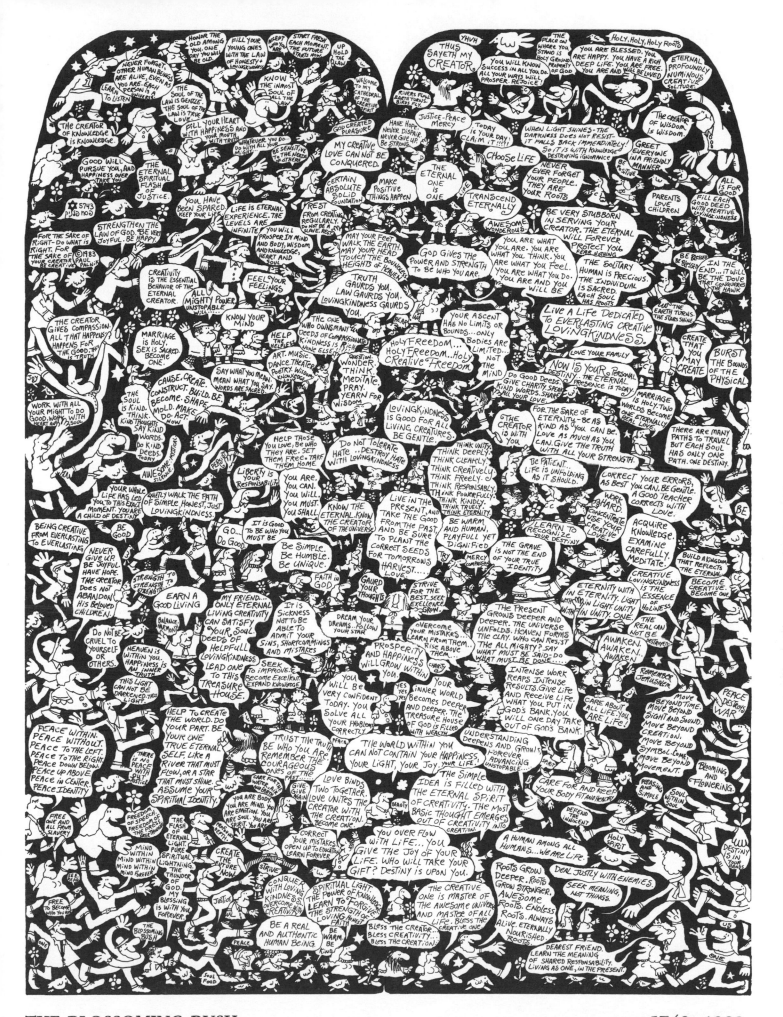

THE BLOSSOMING BUSH   5743–1983

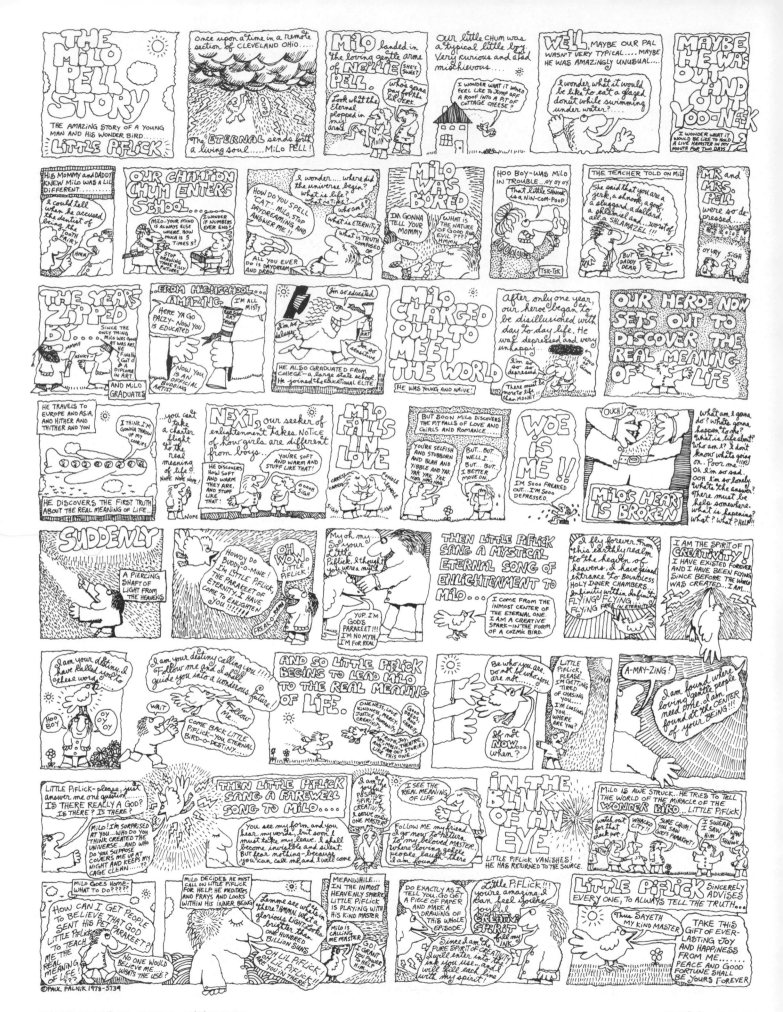

THE MILO PELL STORY

5739–1978

RABBI CUPCAKE'S SERAPH   5738–1978

EXCUSES
42 PATHETIC ATTEMPTS TO EXPLAIN WHAT WENT WRONG!

BERNARDO McDILL
My belongings are spread all over my home and nothing is put away BECAUSE I have memorized exactly where each item is located beCAUSE GOD instructed me to place them there......

PRESIDENT FECAL
We dropped the BOMB because we were absolutely sure that they were about to drop the BOMB on us. People like that are extremely DANGEROUS. It's a good thing we incinerated them first. WE ONLY KILLED 100 Million BARBARIANS.

FOSTA FAZOOL SCHWARTZ
I'm late because I stopped to save an old person from being pummeled into a cole slaw like substance by THE MOTOR OIL PIG BOYS CYCLE GANG. I fought them off one at a time even though 2 MOTOR OIL PIG BOYS BIT ME ON THE CALF.

MAYNARD MAZELTOV
The WORK didn't get done because my uncle, VOSCO VERIPOPPA called, and asked me to take him to the EMERGENCY ROOM at the hospital to HAVE a cocker spaniel named "NORDLEW" removed from HIS LEFT NOSTRIL.

BUGS ROPER
I failed the test because I kept thinking of the tragedy of starving MUSKLER GOATS in SOUTHERN UTAH.

LUGGARD WARTMORE
The reason I lost the game is because I had emergency brain and spine surgery this morning and it slowed me down. Thats the only way I could have lost. Normally I would have WON BIG.

MILO TISH
I DIDN'T SHOW UP BECAUSE I WAS HIT BY A LOW FLYING BLIMP.

EGGS NUNYONZ
I am not successful at the projects I attempt because the world is prejudiced against ignorant, lazy, and INADEQUATE people like myself. Just because I am a quitter at tasks that demand the most out of me, it doesn't mean I can't HUSTLE CHICKS. I love to take THE GUTLESS path but I never quite know where I am going. I act MACHO and tell lies. I cheat and cut corners whenever I can...THE CHICKS NEVER KNOW I'M A PUTZ.

KITTY NULLENVOID
I never THINK, because then I might notenjoy being a PARTY KIND of PERSON in the sort that likes the VACUITY and MEANINGLESS JABBER of PHONIES.

DIRK PECK
I shot LAZLO because his neighbor made a nasty comment about my shoes.

LOINS THRUSTELBAUM
I'm not an international sex symbol because I will not pose nude with VERONICA ZUZZNUKT. I don't care how much money they offer me. One must draw the line somewhere. What PRICE GLORY?

KISHKA GOLDMAN
My life is a total waste because I was born THIRTY CENTURIES ahead of my time, and no one around here even knows that I could have been president of THE COZMIC GLAND CLUB.

RITA QUIPH
I went MAD because my husband is A CHINLESS, PHONEY, UNDER ACHIEVER...WITH A BIG EGO AND A BIG MOUTH.

OLLY SUSK
I fell on your pet PARAKEET and squashed it when I stripped while going to answer the phone.

MYRNA SWIFTCRACKER
I'm sorry I forgot your birthday but a HUGE BOWL of STEAMIN' HOT GOOZLER spilled all over my calendar and blotted out the date!!! Tiny little bugs came to land on the gooey mess. I think they were GOOZLER GNATS. ONE OF THE GNATS STUNG ME. OUCH.

SQUIGGLES NOCTURN HE'S SO ILL
My SEX LIFE is a total bore because sex is a really UGLY, nasty and vulgar EXPERIENCE. Getting to know another person intimately in a loving and sincere authentic sexual union is just plain DIRTY. It's the work of the DEVIL. Evil sinners crave SEX. I have no desire to do evil LIKE YOU. Besides, the opposite sex is just SIMPLY NOT ATTRACTED TO ME! That's why I abuse myself.

BILL NORMAL
I am amazingly AVERAGE because being unique and different scares the BOOGERS outta me. Television tells me what to do, what to buy and WHAT TO BELIEVE! I CRAVE MEDIOCRITY.

BRENDA PAPST
I have NO DATES because ALL THE MEN in this part of the world ARE Socio-PATHIC SEX CRAZY SKITZOIDS that drool!! THEY ALL HAVE BAD GAS. They all have SKIN RASHES and B.O.

SOLLY ZANZIBAR
It wasn't my fault that I lost my job. They didn't understand my NO-WORK, NO PRODUCTIVITY and uncanny SLOTH CREDO. The only reason I missed so many work days was because I had to go to Europe to accept the DEL DONDO AWARD FOR FAR-OUTNESS and COUTH.

PUFFLES WEAVER
I didn't get a raise because my boss is DUMBER than LINT...and besides everyone who gets ahead in my job has to BELONG TO THE FLOWING AND WINDING WOODS COUNTRY CLUB and BANQUET HALL. They also have to CHUM-UP to that miserable PATZ and SHNOOK MORRIE WOYCE (WHAT A SNAKE) HE OWNS THE COMPANY. Also I didn't go to the PARTY that the office manager gave for AL ZUSKY. I'M SO FRUSTRATED

FIDO LOBEY
I can't pay the Bill because I have just donated a VAST FORTUNE to the DOCTOR JULES HUFFNAGY HOME FOR THE EMOTIONALLY SQUASHED and MENTALLY DRAINED, in POBAH HEIGHTS. SQUASHED AND DRAINED. THEY GAVE ME A PLAQUE. I'M SO PROUD.

GREGORY CLAM
We can't go out tonight because I am expecting the universe to come to an end and I haven't packed my bags yet... Besides the results of my saliva test came back and the results show that anyone who kisses me will get a strange TONGUE and LIP DISEASE called TUNG'WIP FREET DUM.

JACKSON SWIGLER
The only reason I wound up in prison was because one 60 year old woman bank teller leaped out of her window, wrestled me TO THE FLOOR and REPEATEDLY BANGED my HEAD AGAINST A DESK. She claims I GAVE HER A HOLD-UP note. WHO COULD HAVE GUESSED IT...WOW. SHE BEAT ME TO A BLOODY PULP. I'M LUCKY TO BE ALIVE!!!

PICKLES TROTSKI
The reason I am not rich is because worldly comforts really turn me off. I'm heavy into poverty as a personal ideal. Food that tastes good and warm clothes are a real bummer. I am disgusted by nice homes and comfortable quiet cars. Vacations make me sick. I think we should share all wealth with everyone...THATS WHY I'M NOT RICH...YUP!

DR. BIFF NAZELHURST
The reason I have such a difficult time showing my feelings and being affectionate is because I'm only concerned with what I can get out of any given situation. No one else counts except me. Most people aren't capable of living up to the HIGH STANDARDS I set for them anyhow...so why waste my VALUABLE time on JERKS.

BABS PUBEFISHY
My life is a miserable AND stinking messy quagmire because I do what EVERYONE ELSE DOES. I go along with the MAJORITY. What they WEAR – I WEAR. What they speak – I SPEAK... how they behave – I BEHAVE. I would NEVER HAVE AN UNPOPULAR OPINION. Blending in' is my MOTTO. Being an INSIGNIFICANT little TWIT is BETTER than the nightmare of REJECTION BY....THEM.

GREGORY CLAM (see above)

HERMAN BOVINE
I did NOT RECEIVE THE AWARD because the ballot box was tampered with by the LEAGUE TO PREVENT CREATIVE LIVING, and by the ORGANIZATION To FURTHER ADVANCE SAMENESS, STAGNATION, PETRIFICATION, INSECURITY, and RIGIDITY. FORGET IT! BALLOT BOX

DALE PHAPHAPH
I lost the race because when I was coming into the home stretch near the finish line, I stepped on a tiny RHODENT, squashed it, and SLIPPED ON THE INNARDS!

BUZZY GENTILE
The BOWLING ALLEY sued me because my BOWLING BALL accidently went into the snack bar and knocked several surprised KEGLERS silly. One of them got steamin HOT NACHO CHEESE IN HIS FACE. IT WASN'T MY FAULT. THE BALL WAS GREASY.

KAH-KAH-POO RINALDI
EYE not responsible for my BEHAVIOR because EYE ARE completely WHACKO and EYE IS fully out of touch with my feelings and reality. EYE never live in the here and now and EYE refuse to accept myself for who and what I am...THATS WHY EYE MADE A KAH-KAH-POO ON THE RUG and SOFA AT GRAND MAS.

GILES KAYMART
I never read Books because its too much effort to concentrate and use my mind. I would rather watch soap operas and hour long police car chase scenes on television. I LIKE QUIZ AND GAME SHOWS too. BOOKS ARE NO WHERE!!!

BELLA PUSTULE
I wasn't invited because my destiny does not include standing in the presence of UGLY and IGNORANT people.

TUBBS LARGO
THE REASON THAT I GAINED SO MUCH WEIGHT IS BECAUSE I HAVEN'T MOVED MY BOWELS IN ALMOST EIGHT MONTHS. I'M SO VERY VERY UNCOMFORTABLE.

HONEY EXPIG
I don't look FABULOUS TODAY because a swarm of PIMPLES swarmed onto my perfect face. I got the pimples from holding Miles Nungelmyne's pet TOAD; PHOTON.

LOLA POLKY
I burned all the cooking because my entire PHYSICAL BODY began to quiver and vibrate. Then a voice rang out from somewhere in MY kitchen. The voice said "DISH PAN HANDS ARE A SIN" BUY FLUFFY SOAP". So I immediately ran TO THE STORE to buy some FLUFFY.

HARLEY FIG
My car ran out of gas because I lost my wallet and all my CREDIT CARDS were in it and I couldn't buy gas, that's why I was late for our meeting. I also lost MY DENTURES in DETROIT.

BABE TEETERBURRO
I don't believe in the ONE CREATOR of the UNIVERSE because if there really is a GOD then for sure HE would make me rich and famous and HE would never let anything happen bad to such a WONDERFUL person as myself. He would get me a new imported SPORTS CAR TOO.

MINNIE MUSKBART
The only reason that I flunked my DRIVERS EXAM was because the HI-WAY PATROLMAN got his legs stuck under my car after the vehicle stopped flipping down the hill. DO I PASS? He was nearly steaming.

CHIP PARKERSBURG
I'm shallow, plastic and empty because I'm a LOUSY, STINKING, ROTTEN, HUNK of MEAT WITH NO SOUL or HEART. I'm into BIG BUCKS, SELF INDULGENCE and RANDOM SEX with STRANGERS. Frankly, I don't have the time to give a DAMN about anyone else but me. I'm into having a GOOD TIME... That what it's all about! FUN

MORTY BALLDOCCI
The ACCIDENT occured because a space man was in the back seat of my car and I caught him calling MARS.

JILL TOAD
I DIDN'T RETURN YOUR CALL BECAUSE MY TELEPHONE CAUGHT FIRE. WHAT A BLAZE.

© 1983 PAUL PALNIK 5743

If no one ever buys this drawing it's because people don't want to hear about how WE FOOL OURSELVES, at least they DON'T WANT to hear about it enough to BUY THIS POSTER. If no one buys this cartoon, than I am fooling myself right now...OH NO!!!! I've been WORKING ON THIS DRAWING FOR WEEKS! PEOPLE JUST DON'T WANT TO HEAR IT. IT'S A Tough Job BUT SOMEONE MUST DO IT!!!

EXCUSES

5743-1983

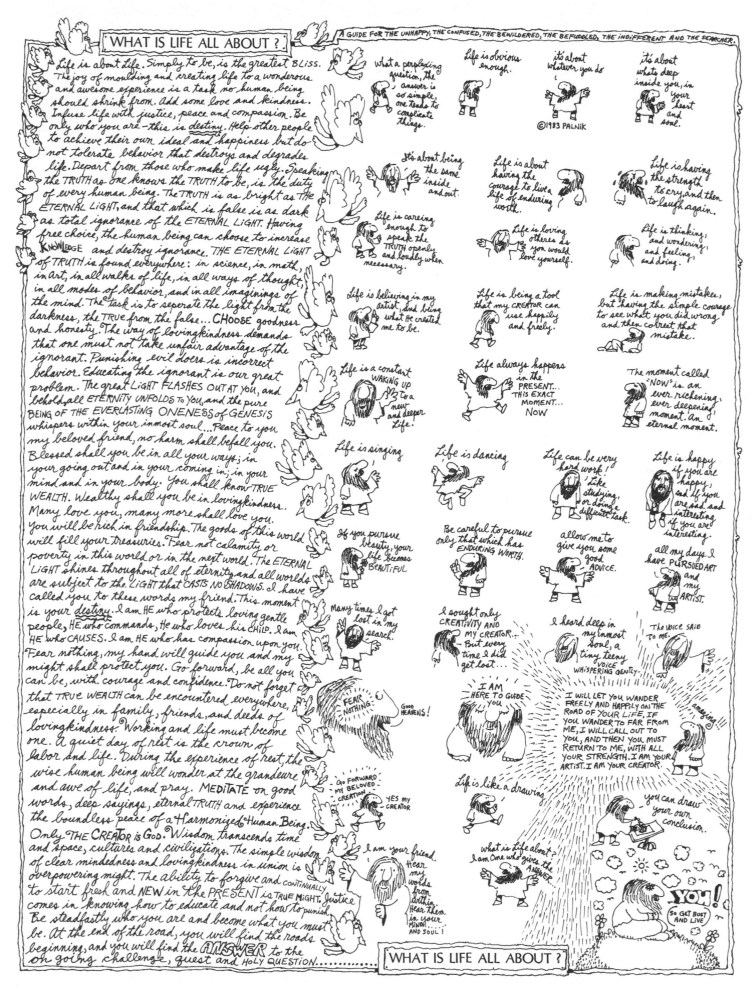

YOU

LIBERATED WOMEN

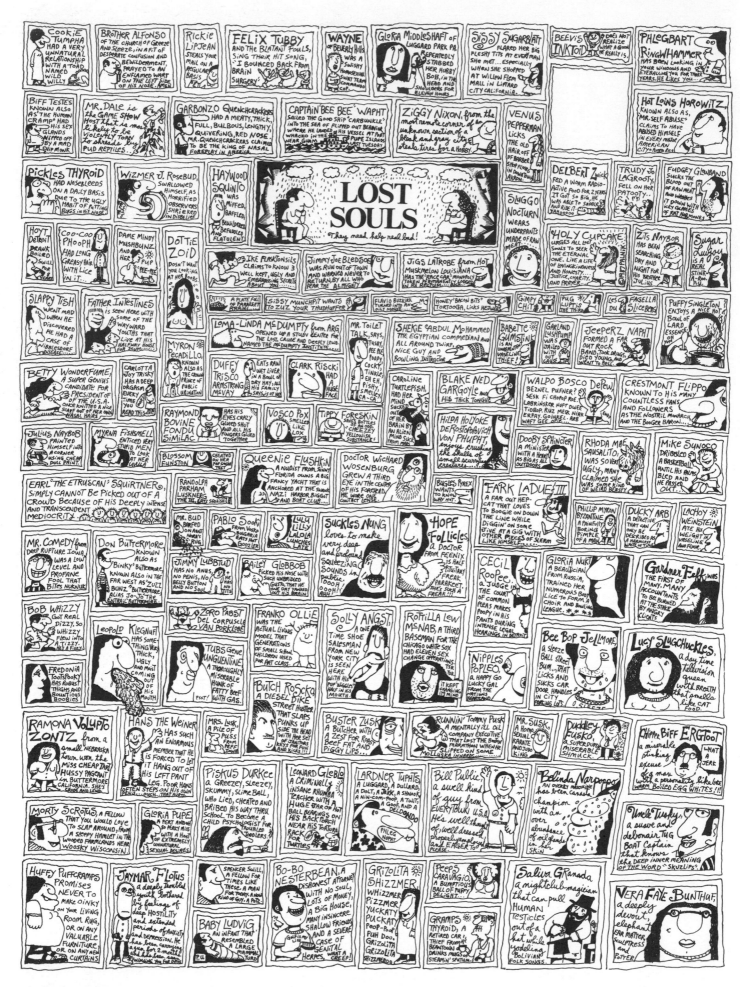

LOST SOULS

5747–1987

THE GREAT NAKED PEOPLE CHASE AND JAMBOREE 5740–1980

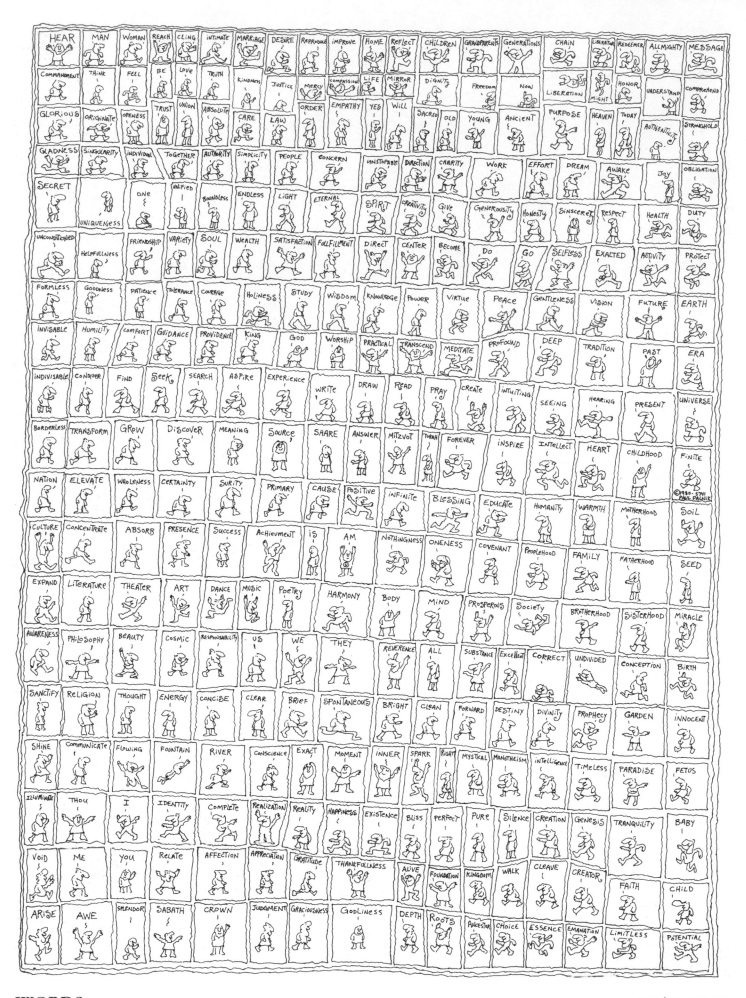

WORDS

5741–1980

THE SANITY STAMPEDE

THE FACTS OF LIFE

5747–1987

The Eternal Knows

(So you better be good)

THE ETERNAL KNOWS

5747–1987

THE HUMAN RACE

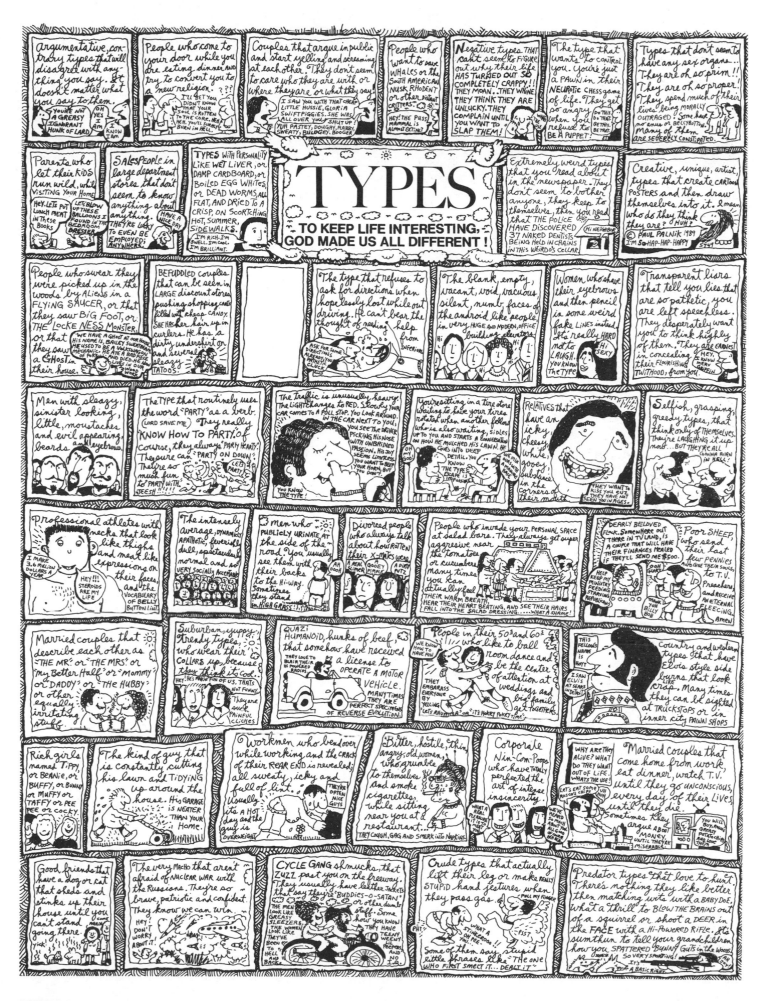

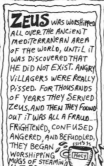

THE UNTOLD STORY 5751–1991

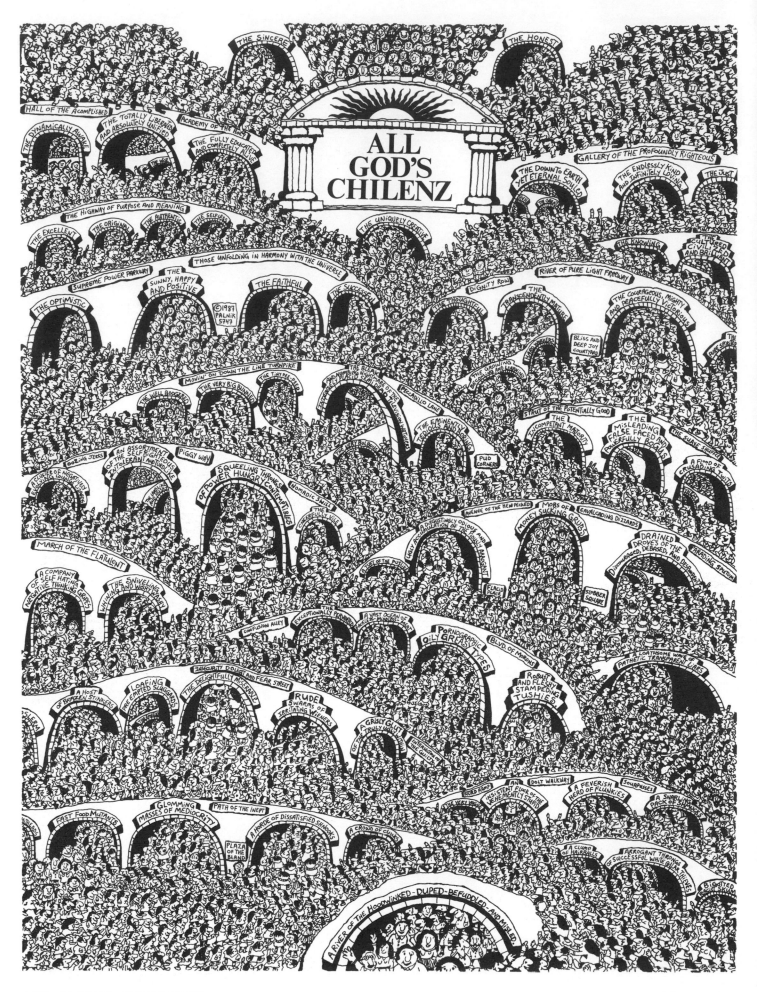

ALL GOD'S CHILLENZ 5747–1987

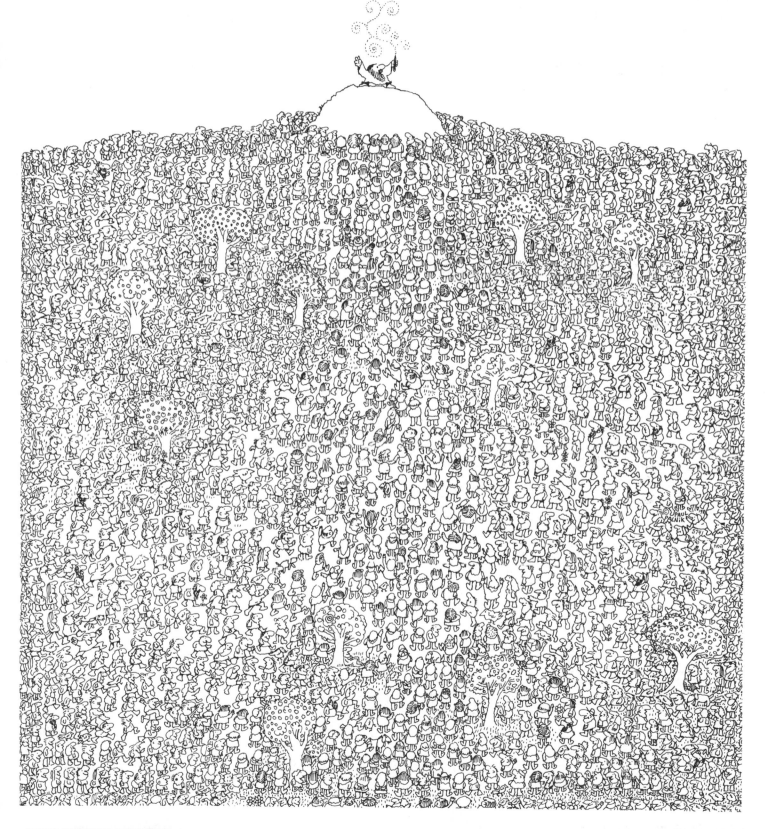

CREATIVE BEING

5743–1983

AFTERWORD

Paul Palnik's art carries with it an inspiring message for men and women today. For amidst the pervasive gloom and cynicism of our times, his posters affirm the joys of life and the existence of a moral order to the universe. In contrast to the art around us that denigrates and makes us feel smaller, Palnik's work celebrates in countless forms our creative powers and our capacity for strength.

In some of his posters, human ambition is satirized, but gently and with understanding. Within our yearnings for outward success, he discerns a deeper motive to make the world a better place in our own particular way. In other posters, he praises the simple virtures of sports and recreational activities, when these are enjoyed with fervor and light-heartedness. Still other posters manage to capture some of the ironies and absurdities in our everyday world and thereby render these a bit easier to handle in our next venture.

For me, though, Paul Palnik's art is most evocative when he casts religious and Biblical themes through his own unique perspective. Though he draws from classic spiritual themes for the most part, he is able to tap what is truly universal and put us in closer touch with the Holy Source inside us. The Prophet is one of his favorite motifs, for Palnik knows that the Prophets of old have words of import for us today. Yet, he is never "holier-than-thou" in his perspective and instinctively senses the love that must exist between a creator and his creation. In fact, many of Palnik's posters explore in subtle ways this complex relationship; always, though, he maintains a proverbial "twinkle-in-the-eye" as he reflects on such lofty matters.

In his poster, "Proverbs," Paul Palnik writes, "Giving makes one rich. Taking leads to poverty. Give your life to life and receive life." We can only be thankful that he has chosen to enrich our lives through his artistic endeavors.

Dr. Edward Hoffman
New York, New York

The original drawings of the works pictured in this book are on deposit in the collection of THE JAMES THURBER LIBRARY FOR COMMUNICATION AND GRAPHIC ARTS, at the WEXNER CENTER of THE OHIO STATE UNIVERSITY, in COLUMBUS, OHIO.

All drawings in this book are 18 × 24.

Paul Palnik, born in Cleveland, Ohio in 1946, received a Bachelor of Fine Arts and a Master of Arts degree in Graphics from The Ohio State University in Columbus. He has worked as an artist and writer for American Greeting Corp. in Cleveland and as an illustrator for The Jerusalem Post in Israel. He has taught drawing and graphics at the University of Arkansas in Fayetteville, Arkansas, at Anderson College in Anderson, Indiana and as a special lecturer in cartooning for the Columbus, Ohio City Schools. His cartoons have appeared in numerous publications and his work is represented in collections in the U.S. and abroad. Palnik exhibits his work in art shows throughout the U.S. and is always adding new works to his ever increasing collection. He lives quietly with his wife and children in Columbus, Ohio.

To order posters, books, or catalogs,
please contact the artist.

PAUL PALNIK
P.O. BOX 09342
COLUMBUS, OHIO
43209
(800) 227-8666   (614) 239-8710

PEACE